BoE 3996

# HANS-GÜNTER HEUMANN

# Das Zauberklavier
## THE MAGIC PIANO

**Für kleine Klavierspieler in Begleitung des Lehrers.**

**Das allererste Zusammenspiel wird zur reinsten Zauberei.**

**For Young Pianists Accompanied by Teachers.**

**The Very First Music Making Is the Purest Magic.**

## Heft 1 / Book 1

## INHALT / CONTENTS

# BOSWORTH EDITION

## Vorwort

Dieses Spielheft ist zum allerersten gemeinsamen Musizieren für kleine Klavierspieler und ihre Lehrer erarbeitet worden.

Um Freude und Eifer des Klavieranfängers zu wecken, bietet die vorliegende Sammlung in einmaliger Weise bekannte und beliebte Musikstückchen an, die für den Neuling am Instrument leicht spielbar sind und durch den gehaltvolleren *Secondo-Part* des Lehrers schon zum akustischen Vergnügen werden.

Langjährige Unterrichtspraxis hat gezeigt, daß besonders der Klavierspieler beim gemeinsamen Musizieren Schwierigkeiten hat, weil ihm sein Instrument natürlich alle polyphonen Möglichkeiten offenbart und er dadurch seltener als andere Instrumentalisten das Zusammenspiel sucht.

Alle hier enthaltenen Spielstücke des *Primo-Parts* befinden sich in der sogenannten 'Anfangs-Handgrundstellung', in der der Schüler mit beiden Daumen vom eingestrichenen C (c¹) aus seine übrigen Finger auf die entsprechend folgenden Nachbartasten gruppiert. Diese 'Anfangs-Handgrundstellung' bietet bereits die Möglichkeit, eine Fülle schöner Melodien zu spielen.

Der Schüler bemühe sich jedoch aufs gründlichste (vor dem Zusammenspiel), seinen *Primo-Part* rhythmisch und melodisch einwandfrei vorzutragen, und zwar zunächst in der angegebenen Notierung. Die Oktavierung ergibt sich erst beim Zusammenspiel mit dem *Secondo-Part*. Aus lesetechnischen Gründen habe ich die Notierung für den Schüler in der gewohnten kleinen bis eingestrichenen Oktave angegeben.

Ein zweites vierhändiges Spielheft mit weiteren bekannten und beliebten Stücken schließt sich in fortführender Schwierigkeit an.

Doch nun viel Spaß und Freude am ersten gemeinsamen Musizieren.

H.-G. H.

## Foreword

This volume of pieces offers the piano beginner the earliest possible opportunity for music making with his or her teacher.

In order to spark the enthusiasm of the beginner, the collection comprises single melodic line versions of famous and well loved musical works which are simple to play for the piano novice and which, in combination with the more complex writing for the *Secondo/Teacher* part, create a satisfying complete texture.

Years of teaching experience have demonstrated to me that pianists have particular difficulties in coping with ensemble playing; naturally, the solo piano offers every polyphonic possibility so the pianist is less enclined to seek out other instrumentalists for performance.

For the player of the *Primo-Part*, all the pieces in this collection are written in the so-called 'resulting base hand position' in which the pupil places both of his or her thumbs over the middle-C, and the other notes correspond step by step, up and down with each finger of each hand, thereby giving the player the scope to produce an abundance of beautiful melodies.

Nevertheless, right from the start, even before playing in duet, the pupil should take care to practise the *Primo part* strictly with regard to rhythm and melody, not departing from what is written. It is only necessary to heed the *8va* instruction when playing in duet; for purposes of easy reading, therefore, I have scored the pupil's part in a more familiar area of the stave.

A second volume of duets with further famous pieces and in more advanced idiom follows this.

Meanwhile, enjoy your first experience of music making together.

H.-G. H.

# Yankee Doodle

**Secondo**

Amerikanisches Volkslied, entstanden um 1775/
American folk song, originating app. 1775
**Arr.: Hans-Günter Heumann**

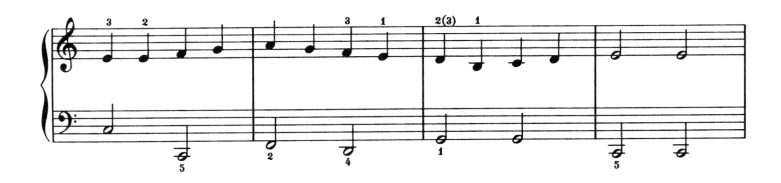

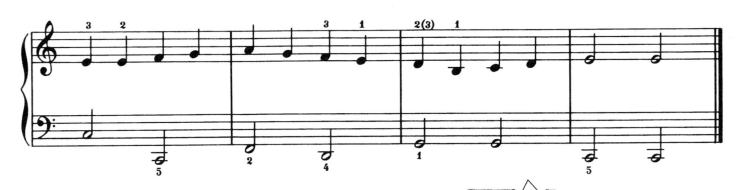

B. & Co. 24 842

# Yankee Doodle

Amerikanisches Volkslied, entstanden um 1775/
American folk song, originating app. 1775
Arr.: Hans-Günter Heumann

**Primo**

Giocoso M.M. ♩ = 138-144

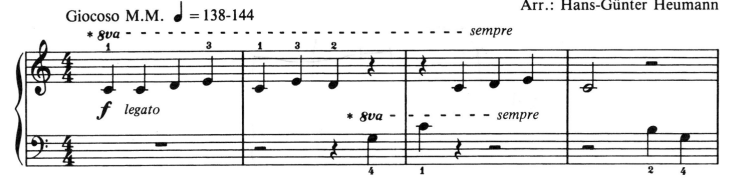

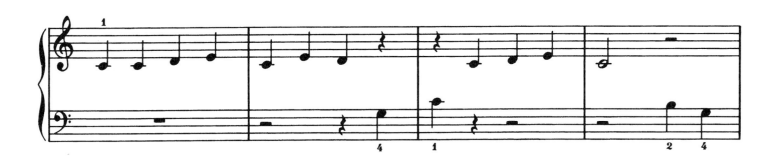

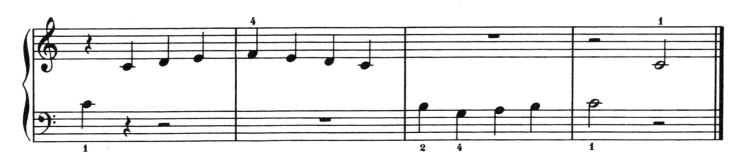

*) Anmerkung für den Lehrer: Aus lesetechnischen Gründen erscheint die Notierung für den Schüler in der kleinen bis eingestrichenen Oktave. Diese Noten müssen jedoch beim vierhändigen Zusammenspiel während des gesamten Stückes oktaviert werden. Allerdings sollte der Schüler beim Üben ohne Oktavierung spielen, um in seiner gewohnten Ausgangslage(in der Mitte des Klaviers) zu bleiben.

*) Teacher's Notes: For the purposes of reading technique, the notation of the pupil's part includes the 8va instruction. This should be heeded throughout only when the pieces are played as duets. When the pupil is practising alone, he or she should ignore it and concentrate on improving his or her knowledge of the familiar section of the keyboard, i.e. the middle range.

# Old McDonald Had a Farm

**Secondo**

Amerikanisches Volkslied/
American folk song
Arr.: Hans-Günter Heumann

# Old McDonald Had a Farm

**Primo**

Amerikanisches Volkslied/
American folk song
Arr.: Hans-Günter Heumann

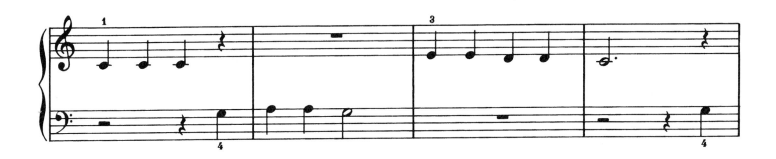

*) Anmerkung für den Lehrer: Aus lesetechnischen Gründen erscheint die Notierung für den Schüler in der kleinen bis eingestrichenen Oktave. Diese Noten müssen jedoch beim vierhändigen Zusammenspiel während des gesamten Stückes oktaviert werden. Allerdings sollte der Schüler beim Üben ohne Oktavierung spielen, um in seiner gewohnten Ausgangslage (in der Mitte des Klaviers) zu bleiben.

*) Teacher's Notes: For the purposes of reading technique, the notation of the pupil's part includes the 8va instruction. This should be heeded throughout only when the pieces are played as duets. When the pupil is practising alone, he or she should ignore it and concentrate on improving his or her knowledge of the familiar section of the keyboard, i.e. the middle range.

# Freude schöner Götterfunken

## The Hymn to Joy

### aus der 9. Symphony

Secondo

Ludwig van Beethoven (1770-1827)
Arr.: Hans-Günter Heumann

# Freude schöner Götterfunken

## The Hymn to Joy

### aus der 9. Symphony

Ludwig van Beethoven (1770-1827)
Arr.: Hans-Günter Heumann

Primo

*) Anmerkung für den Lehrer: Aus lesetechnischen Gründen erscheint die Notierung für den Schüler in der kleinen bis eingestrichenen Oktave. Diese Noten müssen jedoch beim vierhändigen Zusammenspiel während des gesamten Stückes oktaviert werden. Allerdings sollte der Schüler beim Üben ohne Oktavierung spielen, um in seiner gewohnten Ausgangslage(in der Mitte des Klaviers) zu bleiben.

*) Teacher's Notes: For the purposes of reading technique, the notation of the pupil's part includes the 8va instruction. This should be heeded throughout only when the pieces are played as duets. When the pupil is practising alone, he or she should ignore it and concentrate on improving his or her knowledge of the familiar section of the keyboard, i.e. the middle range.

# London Bridge

**Secondo**

Englisches Volkslied/English folk song
Arr.: Hans-Günter Heumann

# London Bridge

**Primo**

Englisches Volkslied/English folk song
Arr.: Hans-Günter Heumann

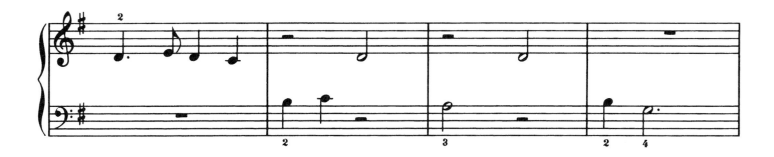

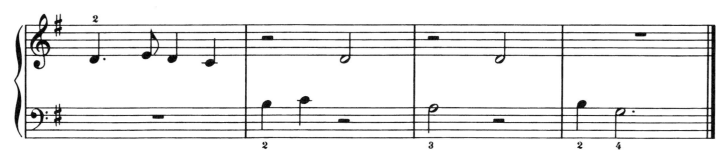

*) Anmerkung für den Lehrer: Aus lesetechnischen Gründen erscheint die Notierung für den Schüler in der kleinen bis eingestrichenen Oktave. Diese Noten müssen jedoch beim vierhändigen Zusammenspiel während des gesamten Stückes oktaviert werden. Allerdings sollte der Schüler beim Üben ohne Oktavierung spielen, um in seiner gewohnten Ausgangslage(in der Mitte des Klaviers) zu bleiben.

*) Teacher's Notes: For the purposes of reading technique, the notation of the pupil's part includes the 8va instruction. This should be heeded throughout only when the pieces are played as duets. When the pupil is practising alone, he or she should ignore it and concentrate on improving his or her knowledge of the familiar section of the keyboard, i.e. the middle range.

# Nobody Knows the Trouble I've Seen

**Secondo**

Negro-Spiritual
Arr.: Hans-Günter Heumann

# Nobody Knows the Trouble I've Seen

### Primo

Negro-Spiritual
Arr.: Hans-Günter Heumann

Moderato M.M. ♩ = 108

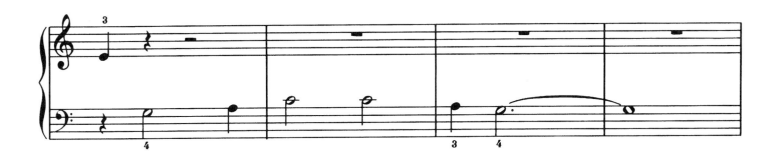

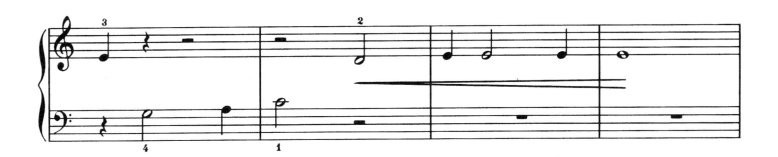

*) Anmerkung für den Lehrer: Aus lesetechnischen Gründen erscheint die Notierung für den Schüler in der kleinen bis eingestrichenen Oktave. Diese Noten müssen jedoch beim vierhändigen Zusammenspiel während des gesamten Stückes oktaviert werden. Allerdings sollte der Schüler beim Üben ohne Oktavierung spielen, um in seiner gewohnten Ausgangslage(in der Mitte des Klaviers) zu bleiben.

*) Teacher's Notes: For the purposes of reading technique, the notation of the pupil's part includes the 8va instruction. This should be heeded throughout only when the pieces are played as duets. When the pupil is practising alone, he or she should ignore it and concentrate on improving his or her knowledge of the familiar section of the keyboard, i.e. the middle range.

# Menuett
## MINUET

Secondo

Jean Philippe Rameau (1683-1764)
Arr.: Hans-Günter Heumann

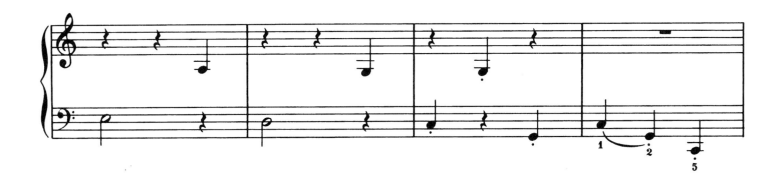

# Menuett

## MINUET

**Primo**

Jean Philippe Rameau (1683-1764)
Arr.: Hans-Günter Heumann

Moderato M.M. ♩ = 108-112

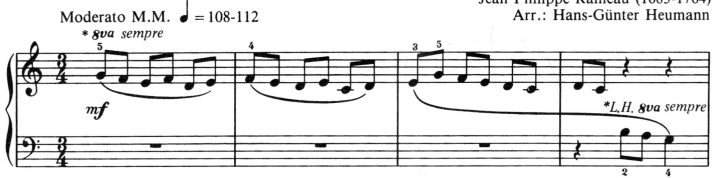

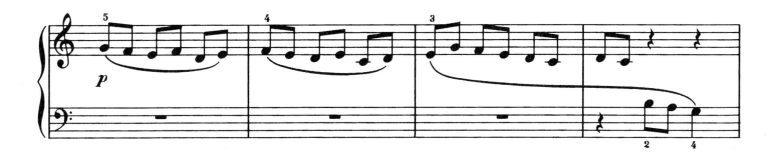

*) Anmerkung für den Lehrer: Aus lesetechnischen Gründen erscheint die Notierung für den Schüler in der kleinen bis eingestrichenen Oktave. Diese Noten müssen jedoch beim vierhändigen Zusammenspiel während des gesamten Stückes oktaviert werden. Allerdings sollte der Schüler beim Üben ohne Oktavierung spielen, um in seiner gewohnten Ausgangslage(in der Mitte des Klaviers) zu bleiben.

*) Teacher's Notes: For the purposes of reading technique, the notation of the pupil's part includes the 8va instruction. This should be heeded throughout only when the pieces are played as duets. When the pupil is practising alone, he or she should ignore it and concentrate on improving his or her knowledge of the familiar section of the keyboard, i.e. the middle range.

# Alouette

**Secondo**

Französisches Volkslied/French folk song
Arr.: Hans-Günter Heumann

Allegretto M.M. ♩ = 112-116

B. & Co. 24 842

# Alouette

**Primo**

Französisches Volkslied/French folk song
Arr.: Hans-Günter Heumann

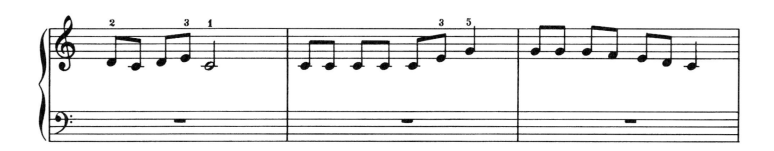

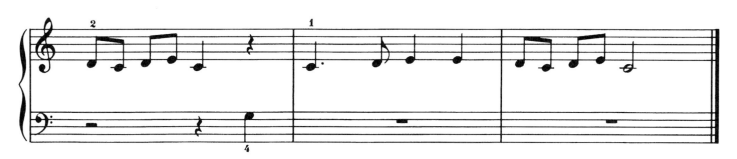

*) Anmerkung für den Lehrer: Aus lesetechnischen Gründen erscheint die Notierung für den Schüler in der kleinen bis eingestrichenen Oktave. Diese Noten müssen jedoch beim vierhändigen Zusammenspiel während des gesamten Stückes oktaviert werden. Allerdings sollte der Schüler beim Üben ohne Oktavierung spielen, um in seiner gewohnten Ausgangslage(in der Mitte des Klaviers) zu bleiben.

*) Teacher's Notes:  For the purposes of reading technique, the notation of the pupil's part includes the 8va instruction. This should be heeded throughout only when the pieces are played as duets. When the pupil is practising alone, he or she should ignore it and concentrate on improving his or her knowledge of the familiar section of the keyboard, i.e. the middle range.

# Oh Susanna

**Secondo**

Stephen C. Foster (1826-1864)
Arr.: Hans-Günter Heumann

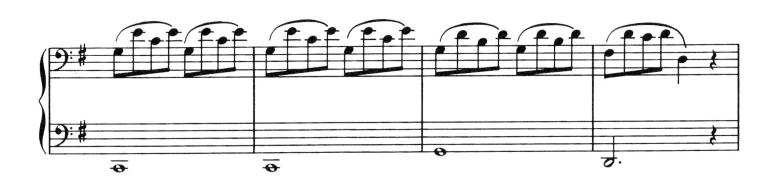

# Oh Susanna

**Primo**

Stephen C. Foster (1826-1864)
Arr.: Hans-Günter Heumann

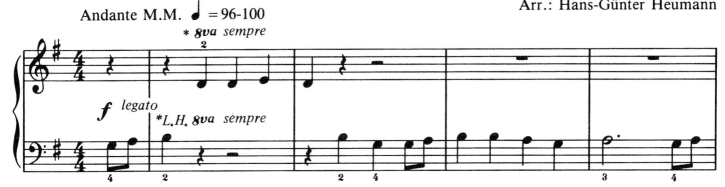

*) Anmerkung für den Lehrer: Aus lesetechnischen Gründen erscheint die Notierung für den Schüler in der kleinen bis eingestrichenen Oktave. Diese Noten müssen jedoch beim vierhändigen Zusammenspiel während des gesamten Stückes oktaviert werden. Allerdings sollte der Schüler beim Üben ohne Oktavierung spielen, um in seiner gewohnten Ausgangslage(in der Mitte des Klaviers) zu bleiben.

*) Teacher's Notes: For the purposes of reading technique, the notation of the pupil's part includes the 8va instruction. This should be heeded throughout only when the pieces are played as duets. When the pupil is practising alone, he or she should ignore it and concentrate on improving his or her knowledge of the familiar section of the keyboard, i.e. the middle range.

# When the Saints Go Marching In

**Secondo**

Amerikanisches Volkslied/American folk song
Arr.: Hans-Günter Heumann

Presto M.M. ♩ = 192-200

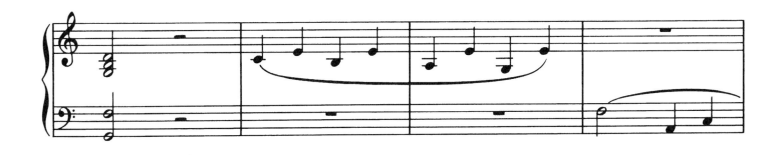

© Copyright MCMLXXXVIII by Bosworth & Co., Berlin
BOSWORTH & CO., BERLIN - LONDON

B. & Co. 24 842

# When the Saints Go Marching In

**Primo**

Presto M.M. ♩ = 192-200

Amerikanisches Volkslied/American folk song
Arr.: Hans-Günter Heumann

\* *8va sempre*

\*) Anmerkung für den Lehrer: Aus lesetechnischen Gründen erscheint die Notierung für den Schüler in der kleinen bis eingestrichenen Oktave. Diese Noten müssen jedoch beim vierhändigen Zusammenspiel während des gesamten Stückes oktaviert werden. Allerdings sollte der Schüler beim Üben ohne Oktavierung spielen, um in seiner gewohnten Ausgangslage(in der Mitte des Klaviers) zu bleiben.

\*) Teacher's Notes: For the purposes of reading technique, the notation of the pupil's part includes the 8va instruction. This should be heeded throughout only when the pieces are played as duets. When the pupil is practising alone, he or she should ignore it and concentrate on improving his or her knowledge of the familiar section of the keyboard, i.e. the middle range.

# Musette

**Secondo**

Johann Sebastian Bach (1685-1750)
Arr.: Hans-Günter Heumann

# Musette

**Primo**

Johann Sebastian Bach (1685-1750)
Arr.: Hans-Günter Heumann

Allegro M.M. ♩ = 132-144

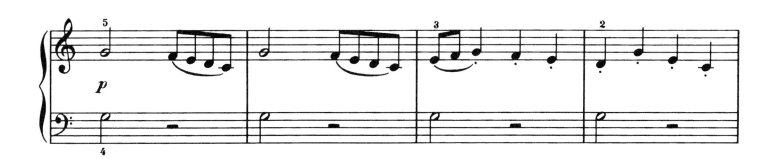

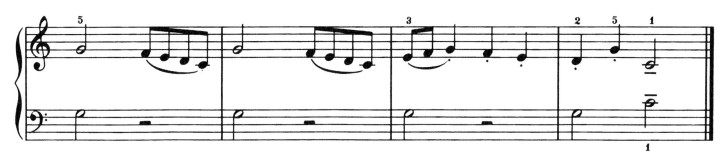

*) Anmerkung für den Lehrer: Aus lesetechnischen Gründen erscheint die Notierung für den Schüler in der kleinen bis eingestrichenen Oktave. Diese Noten müssen jedoch beim vierhändigen Zusammenspiel während des gesamten Stückes oktaviert werden. Allerdings sollte der Schüler beim Üben ohne Oktavierung spielen, um in seiner gewohnten Ausgangslage (in der Mitte des Klaviers) zu bleiben.

*) Teacher's Notes: For the purposes of reading technique, the notation of the pupil's part includes the 8va instruction. This should be heeded throughout only when the pieces are played as duets. When the pupil is practising alone, he or she should ignore it and concentrate on improving his or her knowledge of the familiar section of the keyboard, i.e. the middle range.

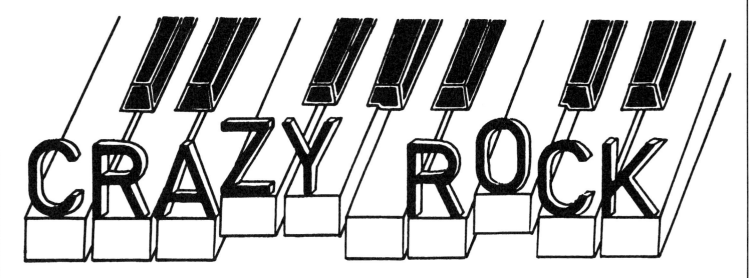

# CRAZY ROCK

Leichte Original-Rock'n'Roll's
und Rock'n'Roll-Bearbeitungen
für Klavier zu vier Händen
u.a. mit
"Jailhouse Rock" +
von

Easy Originals & Arrangements
of Rock'n'Roll's
for Piano Duet
including
"See You Later, Alligator"
by

# Hans-Günter Heumann

Dieses Heft mit leichten Original-Rock'n'Rolls und Rock'n' Roll-Bearbeitungen für Klavier zu vier Händen bietet dem Klavierschüler und Rock'n'Roll-Fan die Möglichkeit, diesen vitalen Musikstil im typischen Klang und Rhythmus nachzuvollziehen.

Der Rock'n'Roll (R&R) entstand Anfang der 50er Jahre unseres Jahrhunderts in den USA aus einer Mischung des 'Rhythm & Blues' (R&B) der Farbigen und dem 'Country & Western' (C&W) der Weißen.

Der musikalische Aufbau des R&R ist einfach und prägnant und richtet sich häufig nach dem zwölftaktigen Blues-Harmonieschema.

Da der R & R vom rhythmischen Element lebt, ist besonders im Secondo-Part auf einen absolut gleichmäßigen und kräftigen Beat bei genauer Akzentuierung und Artikulation zu achten.

Der Primo-Part ist durch häufige rhythmische Einwürfe im 'Off-Beat' (= rhythmisches Akzentmuster, das durch Verschiebung gegen den Grundschlag entsteht) besonders interessant.

Das Pedal wird im R & R sehr sparsam gebraucht, vorwiegend in langsameren Stücken.

Die Hauptvertreter des Rock 'n'Roll waren: Bill Haley, Elvis Presley, Chuck Berry, Little Richard und Jerry Lee Lewis.

Für den modernen Klavierunterricht stellt diese Ausgabe - neben dem Spiel anderer Musik - eine anregende Ergänzung und Bereicherung dar und bringt viel Spaß und Freude am Musizieren.

With this book of easy Rock'n'Roll originals and arrangements for Piano Duet, piano pupils and Rock'n' Roll fans can get the feel of the typical sounds and rhythms of this important musical idiom.

Rock'n'Roll has its roots in America in the early 1950s, the mixture of black Rhythm and Blues and white Country and Western.

Its musical construction is simple, its harmonic scheme basically the twelve-bar Blues. The soul of Rock'n' Roll is its rhythm, the Secondo part here best demonstrating the point with its rigorous, powerful beat and precise accents and articulation. So, all the interesting melodic turns are found in the frequently 'off-beat' Primo part. You will not need to use the pedal much, except in the slow pieces.

Remember the Rock'n' Roll Greats: Bill Haley, Chuck Berry, Elvis Presley, Little Richard and Jerry Lee Lewis.

Used in conjunction with more conventional music, piano lessons should benefit from this stimulating, enriching complementary material. It is also music making that is a lot of fun.

# BOSWORTH EDITION

BoE 3938